Grammar

Grade 6

Reading and writing are the cornerstones of education. The basics of these skills include reading comprehension and a working knowledge of grammar and spelling. Language class, in which students develop their foundation of English, should be an enjoyable educational experience for all students. This is possible, however, only if students are conscious of steady progress in their written language, and if they understand what they are doing.

This *Grammar Grade 6* book is part of a *Basics First* series that has been designed to help students succeed in grammar usage. The activities were created to help students feel confident about their grammar skills and help them understand the steps involved in learning these skills.

The pages have been arranged in an easy-to-follow format. This format allows the teacher to choose from a variety of sixth-grade grammar skills that are presented in an interesting, relevant, and age-appropriate manner. Each skill begins with rules and examples. These are followed by intensive practice with interesting information. The book concludes with review pages to check mastery of the skills learned. The skills included are those that every sixth-grade student should possess in order to be able to express himself or herself confidently in spoken or written English.

With more value being placed on the traditional basic subjects, it is easy to understand the vital role grammar plays in everyone's life. It has become clear how important the teaching of grammar is in helping students to become confident in their English usage.

This book can be used alone or as an integral part of any language program. It can also be used in conjunction with literature-based programs to provide students with the benefits of a well-rounded English program.

Sentence Sense

Name _____

All About Types of Sentences

There are four types of sentences.

A **declarative sentence** makes a statement or tells something. It ends with a period.

Example   *The dinosaurs have been gone for 65 million years.*

An **interrogative sentence** asks a question and ends with a question mark.

Example   *Do you know what happened to the dinosaurs?*

An **imperative sentence** tells or asks someone to do something. It ends with a period.

Example   *Find out why the dinosaurs disappeared.*

An **exclamatory sentence** shows strong feelings or excitement. It ends with an exclamation mark.

Example   *Don't drop the dinosaur bone!*

Some exclamations such as *Wow!, Oh, no!,* and *Of course!* are not complete sentences.
They are called **interjections,** and they also end with an exclamation mark.

Practice Makes Perfect

Write the name of each type of sentence below and label each interjection.

1. People once thought dinosaur bones were the bones of ancient monsters, such as fire-breathing dragons. _____

2. Did fire-breathing dragons truly exist? _____

3. No way! _____

4. Think about what would happen if dinosaurs still roamed the Earth. _____

5. Would they threaten human life? _____

6. There are probably remains of unknown dinosaur species still to be found. _____

7. Will dinosaurs be cloned someday, like in the movies? _____

8. Who knows? _____

9. Be prepared for anything. _____

10. Watch out for T-rex! _____

11. Become a paleontologist. _____

12. You can discover more mysteries of the largest (and some of the smallest) reptiles that ever roamed Earth. _____

Try This!   Write ten sentences about dinosaurs. Make sure you use every type of sentence at least once.

2

FS-30045 Grammar

A Tale of Two Kitties

Name _____

All About Subjects and Predicates

Subjects tell what a sentence is about. In declarative sentences, they usually appear at or near the beginning of the sentence. A **simple subject** is a subject without its modifiers.

Example ▸ *Cats have been domesticated for thousands of years.* The subject is *cats.*

Predicates tell what happened to the subject, what it does, or what it did. The predicate is *have been domesticated for thousands of years*. A **simple predicate** is a verb without its modifiers.

Practice Makes Perfect

Underline the simple subject in each sentence below. Circle the simple predicate.

Example ▸ *The ancient Egyptians revered their cats.*
Egyptians is the simple subject, *revered* is the simple predicate.

Cats are very popular pets in present-day North America. People buy special treats for their cats. They buy cat beds, cat food, and cat scratching posts. But today's cats are not treated well compared to cats in ancient Egypt.

The ancient Egyptians worshiped cats. These felines were thought of as sacred. Egyptians built stone temples to their cats. Many buried cats in coffins. Cats were often mummified and laid to rest in their master's tombs.

Wealthy families sometimes kept several cats as pets. The cats were often treated as well as the children. In many modern countries, cats have dreadful lives. They are left to fend for themselves in the street. They are harmed and even eaten. Cats should not be considered sacred today. But they should be protected and respected as animals with whom we share Earth.

Circle the complete subject and draw a rectangle around the complete predicate in each sentence.

1. In some countries, cows are sacred animals.

2. In India, cows are not to be bothered as they roam the streets.

3. Cows are not eaten as food in India.

4. The expression "sacred cow" has come to mean someone or something that is not to be questioned, that must be accepted.

5. There are many varieties of cows throughout the world.

Try This! Write a story about an imaginary experience you had with your own pet or with another animal. (Example: *The Day the Animals Fed Me at the Zoo.*) Make sure each sentence contains a subject and a predicate.

3

FS-30045 Grammar

Such Fascinating Subjects

Name _____

All About Subjects in Interrogative and Imperative Sentences

Since a question is asked in an interrogative sentence, you often must look carefully for the subject.

Example *Did cats of long ago live in people's homes? Cats,* not *Did* is the subject of the sentence. If you rearrange the sentence so it becomes declarative, you can more easily see the subject. *Cats did live in people's homes.*

Find out about imperative sentences. The subject is really the invisible word *you,* since the sentence really means **You** *find out about imperative sentences.* The word *you* is understood to be in the sentence, so *you* is the subject.

Practice Makes Perfect

Underline the complete subject in each interrogative sentence below. Circle each complete predicate. Example: *Did you know that Steller's sea eagle is the largest and strongest?* Think of this as a declarative sentence: *You did know that Steller's sea eagle is the largest and strongest.* Therefore, *you* is the subject, *did know that Steller's sea eagle is the largest and strongest* is the complete predicate.

1. Are starlings native to North America?

2. Did you hear the birds chirping in the morning?

3. Do you leave birdseed out for them?

4. Did you know that the passenger pigeon is extinct?

5. Is it true that the ostrich cannot fly?

6. Are falcons still found in the wild?

7. Is it true that eagles and hawks have the keenest sight of all birds?

8. Are most bald eagles found in Alaska?

9. Did the dodo become extinct because it was stupid?

10. Did birds exist with dinosaurs?

Write *you* next to the imperative sentences below that are missing the unseen subject *you.*
Circle the subjects in the other types of sentences.

11. Draw a picture of your favorite bird.

12. Find the smallest bird in the world.

13. Did you draw that picture of a robin?

14. Start thinking about your bird report.

15. Look in the *Birds of North America* book.

 Try This! Write five facts about one of the birds listed above.

FS-30045 Grammar

Compound It!

Name _____

All About Compound Subjects and Predicates

Often a sentence will have two subjects and one predicate. These **compound subjects** are better in one, not two sentences.
Example: *The king of Spain believed in the cities of gold.*
The queen of Spain believed in the cities of gold. The two subjects are *the king* and *the queen*. Make a compound sentence by combining the two subjects, using the same predicate and joining them with one of the following conjunctions: **and**, **or**, or **but**. *The king **and** queen of Spain believed in the cities of gold.*

Practice Makes Perfect

Rewrite the sentences below, combining the two sentences into one.

1. The Spanish looked for the Seven Cities of Cibola. A Moorish slave named Estevanico looked for the Seven Cities of Cibola.

   _____

2. Francisco Coronado led an expedition. Estevanico led an expedition.

   _____

3. The Moor hoped to find riches. The Spaniard hoped to find riches.

   _____

4. Estevanico explored Arizona and New Mexico. Coronado explored Arizona and New Mexico.

   _____

Compound predicates have one subject and two predicates. Example: *The explorers wanted to find the treasure. The explorers were competing with each other.* Write one sentence: *The explorers wanted to find the treasure, but were competing with each other.* Using the same subject, connect the two sentences using **and**, **or**, or **but**.

5. Coronado found no riches. Coronado returned to Mexico.

   _____

6. The Zuñi Indians live in the Southwest United States. The Zuñi Indians are found in present-day Gallup, New Mexico.

   _____

7. The Spanish believed in a fairy tale. The Spanish followed a legend about the Seven Cities of Cibola.

   _____

Try This! Draw what you think the Seven Cities of Cibola would look like if they existed. Write about an adventure there and put yourself in it!

⟨5⟩

Let's Change!

Name _____

All About Compound Sentences
Short, simple sentences can be joined by the conjunctions **and**, **but**, **or**, and **nor**. A comma is sometimes used before the conjunction.

 Clocks tell time. They are used for decoration, too.
Change to *Clocks tell time, but they are used for decoration, too.*

Practice Makes Perfect
Read the story below about clocks. There are many places where you can change simple sentences into compound sentences. Rewrite the sentences that you change. Hint: Look for short sentences.

The first real clocks appeared in the 1200s. They had no hands. There was no dial. The word *clock* probably came from the French. The word *cloche* means "bell." There is a German word that's similar to it. This word, *Glocke,* means "bell."

The ancient Romans used clocks. They were water clocks. Water drained from a glass jar. The glass jar had a scale with markings on it. The markings showed how the water level dropped. This marked the time. Sundials are clocks. The sun casts a shadow. It moves across the dial. Time is measured by the length or angle of the shadow.

_____

_____

_____

_____

_____

_____

_____

 Design a clock or watch that you think you could sell. Does your timepiece make noise? Does anything move? What is special about it? Make a three-dimensional model and explain how it works to your friends or classmates.

FS-30045 Grammar

It's Only Proper!

Name _____

All About Common and Proper Nouns
Common nouns name people, places, and things.
Proper nouns name particular people, places, and things.

 Example   *Building* is a noun. *There was a fire in that building.* It could be any building.

The Sears Tower is in Chicago. There is only one Sears Tower.
There is only one Chicago. These are proper nouns. Proper nouns are capitalized.
Common nouns are not.

Practice Makes Perfect
Write factual sentences using proper nouns from the list below.

 Example   World War II and Franklin D. Roosevelt: *Franklin D. Roosevelt was the president of the United States during most of World War II.* Make sure your facts are true. *George Washington was the king of France* would not be true.

Your sentences will most likely also contain some common nouns. Circle the common nouns in your sentences.

Martin Luther King, Jr.	Theodore Roosevelt	Pennsylvania
Paris	New Jersey	Egypt
Lake Michigan	Pike's Peak	"The Star-Spangled Banner"
Panama Canal	North America	Neptune
Garden State	Canada	Francis Scott Key
France	Hershey	Mars
Great Lakes	Sphinx	Nobel Peace Prize

_____

_____

_____

_____

_____

_____

 **Try This!**   Write a story using eight places or people in your town or city.

Nounsense!

Name _____

All About Singular and Plural Nouns

A **singular noun** names one person, place, thing, or idea (*shoe, jacket, thought*). A **plural noun** names more than one person, place, thing, or idea (*shoes, jackets, thoughts*).

To make most singular nouns plural, an **s** is added. If a singular noun ends in **s**, **ss**, **x**, **z**, **ch**, or **sh**, an **es** is added to form a plural (*dress, dresses; mess, messes; fox, foxes; waltz, waltzes; march, marches; wish, wishes*). If a singular noun ends in **a consonant and a y**, the **y** is changed to **i** and **es** is added (*baby, babies; fairy, fairies*). If a singular noun ends with **a vowel and y**, **s** is added to form the plural (*bay, bays; day, days; monkey, monkeys*).

Practice Makes Perfect

Read the story below. Make a list of all the singular nouns that should be plural. Change them to plurals.

SINGULAR	PLURAL
_____	_____
_____	_____
_____	_____
_____	_____
_____	_____
_____	_____
_____	_____
_____	_____
_____	_____
_____	_____
_____	_____
_____	_____
_____	_____
_____	_____
_____	_____
_____	_____
_____	_____
_____	_____
_____	_____
_____	_____
_____	_____

For thousand of year, people have been wearing clothing of some sort. They may not have worn dress, pant, or shirt, but they did wear some form of these item. People began wearing clothing to protect themselves from the weather or to look good to other cave people. People began to wear animal skin. These skin were often a by-product of animal they killed to eat, such as fox, buffalo, or bear. In more modern day, people in different part of the world dressed in local costume. In Scotland, men wore kilt, a type of skirt. In England, women wore huge, wide, skirt and dress. Clothes were made of material such as cotton and wool. Clothing was handmade, but today we buy garment made in factory. Lady clothing has changed from fancy to practical as many women today go to work.

Try This! Write down all the different types of clothing you can think of in both singular and plural forms.

8

FS-30045 Grammar

Make an Exception!

Name _____

All About Exceptional Plurals

Exceptional plurals take exception to the usual rules about plurals and must be learned separately.

English is a language with many exceptions. Sometimes the rules are broken. Nouns that end in **f** or **fe** often become plural by **dropping the f** or **fe** and **adding ves**: (*half, halves; life, lives; loaf, loaves; wolf, wolves*).

However, some nouns that end in **f** can be made plural by **just adding s**: (*roof, roofs; chief, chiefs; belief, beliefs*). Some nouns seem to have no rules. Look at the following strange plurals: *tooth, teeth; foot, feet; child, children; mouse, mice; woman, women; man, men*. There are even a few nouns that don't change at all in the plural (*deer, sheep, moose, news, information, fun*).

Practice Makes Perfect

Change the singular nouns to plural wherever necessary in each sentence below.

1. Our cow gave birth to twin calf. _____
2. Mouse often carry diseases. _____
3. The moose were swimming across the lake. _____
4. The dentist said his tooth were crooked. _____
5. Most woman in the United States have jobs. _____
6. The deer were grazing in the clover. _____
7. The chief of all the tribes gathered together. _____
8. Those child just got out of school. _____
9. Take the sheep to the pasture. _____
10. Two half of an apple make one whole. _____
11. I think those shoes are too big for your foot. _____
12. We need to make two loaf of bread for the party. _____

Plural Review!

Cross out each incorrectly spelled plural and write the correct one on the line provided.

13. Babys are known to cry at the worst times. _____
14. Mouses like to eat cheese and cats like to eat mouses. _____
15. The thiefs were caught as they climbed out the window. _____
16. The band played many waltzs, and everyone danced. _____
17. The churchs in our town held a carnival. _____
18. We could hear the dishs crash to the floor in the restaurant. _____

Try This! Make a singular/plural chart to share with your class.

Missing Parts

Name _____

All About Sentence Fragments

A fragment is a piece of something. It is not complete. A **sentence fragment** looks like a sentence with a capital and a period or other punctuation at the end, but it's not a complete thought and not a sentence. The fragment is missing either its subject or predicate.

Example 1. *A cloud is a mass of small drops of water or ice that.* 2. *Floats in the air.* Number 1 is not a sentence since the predicate, *is a mass of small drops of water or ice that,* is not complete as it ends with *that.* Number 2 isn't a sentence because *Floats in the air* has no subject. Written together, these two fragments form a complete sentence: *A cloud is a mass of small drops of water or ice that floats in the air.*

Practice Makes Perfect

Read the information below about clouds. Write *S* or *P* above each fragment to indicate whether a subject or predicate is missing. Change each fragment to make a complete sentence. There is more than one in most selections, so write *S* or *P* as many times as needed.

1. Clouds are. Important to the changes in weather.

2. Clouds bring necessary. Rainfall and snow to provide water.

3. Clouds come in many. Different forms.

4. White fluffy clouds. Often take the form of familiar shapes.

5. Menacing-looking gray. Or black clouds look threatening.

6. Most clouds. Change their shape all the time.

7. Stratus and stratocumulus clouds. Are seen close to Earth.

8. Some middle clouds that form. Smooth gray sheets across the sky are called altostratus clouds.

9. Other middle clouds like altocumulus clouds. Appear in many shapes.

10. High clouds. Such as cirrus, cirrostratus, and cirrocumulus are formed of ice crystals.

Write *S* for sentence and *F* for fragment next to each.

11. A cirrostratus cloud. Is a thin sheet of cloud. ____

12. Cirrus clouds are delicate clouds that you see high in the sky. ____

13. A cirrostratus cloud often makes a halo appear around the moon. ____

14. Clouds form from. Evaporated water from bodies of water on Earth. ____

Try This!   Go outside on a day when there are clouds in the sky. Draw what shapes, animals, or people the clouds resemble. Then write what types of clouds you think they are.

On and On and On . . .

Name _____

All About Run-on Sentences

Run-on sentences often go on and on without letting the reader stop for a breath. They are usually long sentences that aren't punctuated in the right places and contain lots of **ands.**

 Coin collecting is a popular hobby and many people collect coins and they are called numismatists. You might change this to *Coin collecting is a popular hobby. Many people collect coins. They are called numismatists.* Or *Coin collecting is a popular hobby. Many people collect coins, and they are called numismatists.*

Practice Makes Perfect

Read the paragraph below about coins. Rewrite it to eliminate all run-on sentences.

　　People collect coins for many reasons and some people like to have sets of coins from a particular country and some people even consider them works of art and sometimes people buy them for investment and they sell them for more money when the coins become rare, and many collectors concentrate on a special kind of coin and these might be coins of a certain shape or coins that show a certain subject, such as animals or leaders of a country, and the best way to start a coin collection is to use any change you might have lying around and then you can start swapping with someone who is also interested in coins.

_____

_____

_____

_____

_____

_____

_____

_____

Take out the coins that you may have in your pocket, purse, or piggy bank. Sort them out according to value. Then record the date and what is on each coin. Start your own coin collection.

　　　　　　⟨11⟩　　　　　　FS-30045 Grammar

Possessive Practice

Name _____

All About Possessive Nouns

Nouns name people, places, things, and ideas. They can be singular or plural, and they can also show possession. **Possession** means something belongs to someone. A **possessive noun** shows who or what has something. An **apostrophe and an s** can be added to a singular noun ending in a consonant to make it possessive. (Examples: *The colonist had a large farm. The colonist's farm… George Washington had land. George Washington's land…*) Plural nouns also can become possessive. An **apostrophe added after the s** that makes the noun plural makes a plural noun possessive. (Examples: *The colonists had a rebellion. The colonists' rebellion… The slaves had dreadful lives* or *The dreadful lives of the slaves* becomes *The slaves' dreadful lives…*)

An **apostrophe s** ('s) can be added to plural nouns not ending in s to form the possessive plural. (Examples: *The games of children in colonial times… Children's games in colonial times…* Other examples are *women, women's; men, men's.*)

People's names ending in *s* also follow the rules: *The uniform of James* becomes *James's uniform* because although *James* ends in *s*, the name is singular. *The Simpsons had a general store* becomes *The Simpsons' store* because Simpsons is the plural of Simpsons. If you are referring to one person, it would read as follows: *Simpson's horse got loose.* However, *The Simpsons live here* requires no apostrophe.

Practice Makes Perfect

Change each underlined noun to make it possessive. Write the possessive nouns on the lines.

1. The book of <u>Esther Forbes</u>, *Johnny Tremain*, is about colonial America. _____

2. <u>America</u> had a colonial period from 1607 to 1775. _____

3. The goals of many <u>colonists</u> were freedom and independence. _____

4. The leadership of <u>George Washington</u> was unquestioned. _____

5. The enemies of the <u>Indians</u> were often colonists. _____

6. The children of the <u>settlers</u> usually helped with farming. _____

7. <u>Betsy</u> Ross had a successful sewing business. _____

8. <u>England</u> had thirteen colonies in the New World to govern. _____

9. The property belonging to <u>Germans</u> was often farmland. _____

10. The education of <u>children</u> was usually not long-lasting. _____

Try This!

Using possessive nouns, write a paragraph containing 10 things that belong to people around you. (Example: *The twins' books, my friend's pencil*)

12

Enough About Nouns

Name _____

All About Common, Proper, and Collective Nouns

Common nouns name any person, place, thing, or idea. (*Everything* in the *world* has *color*.)
Proper nouns name a special person, place, thing, or idea. (*Sandra* has a blue dress.)
Collective nouns name a group, or a bunch of things together. (The **pride** of lions ran like a *golden blur across the savannah*.)

Some collective nouns are *a herd of buffalo, a crowd of people, a gaggle of geese, a bunch of carrots, a team of horses.*

Practice Makes Perfect

Find and circle the common nouns in the sentences below. Underline the proper nouns. Using the words in the box below, write the answers to the clues on the lines provided.

1. This is the house in which the President of the United States lives. _____

2. This statue holds a torch and is a greenish color. _____

3. In Washington, D.C., you can see this long, black stone. _____

4. Television shows keep their guests here before they go on. _____

5. This river in Austria has music that is named for it. _____

6. This river forms much of the boundary between Oklahoma and Texas. _____

7. This beautiful forest is a favorite tourist destination in Germany. _____

8. This was a popular cartoon character on TV. _____

9. This country of ice and snow is the opposite of its name. _____

10. In 1787, he was the first person to sail around the world under the American flag. _____

Robert Gray	Green Room	Danube	Pink Panther	Greenland	Red River
Vietnam Veterans Memorial		Statue of Liberty		White House	Black Forest

Collective Nouns

Write the correct collective noun in the sentences below. Use the words in the box to help you.

flock
school
pack
tribe
crowd
stack

11. We saw a _____ of wolves.

12. They lived near a _____ of Indians.

13. The _____ of sheep were shorn yesterday.

14. The _____ of fish swam away when they saw the hook.

15. The _____ of sports fans became rowdy.

16. My _____ of stamps is not very valuable.

Try This!
Make up collective nouns for groups of things you have around.
(Examples: a herd of sports cards, a mess of books, a bunch of tapes)

Replace It!

Name _____

All About Subject and Object Pronouns

A **pronoun** takes the place of one or more nouns. **Subject pronouns** are used as the subject of a sentence. **I**, **you**, **he**, **she**, **it**, **we**, **they** are subject pronouns. (Example: *Secret codes have been around since the time of the ancient Greeks. Secret codes* is the subject, and these words can be replaced with *they. They have been around since the time of the ancient Greeks.*)

Object pronouns replace nouns that are the object of a verb. The object of a verb receives the action of the verb. It answers the question **whom** or **what** following an action verb. (Example: *The Spartans wound a belt in a spiral pattern around a stick.* The subject is *Spartans.* The action verb is *wound,* and the object of that verb is *belt*—it answers the question **what**. *Belt* is replaced by *it.*) Object pronouns are **me**, **you**, **him**, **her**, **you**, **it**, **us**, **them**.

Practice Makes Perfect

Learn about codes as you replace each underlined subject in the sentences below with a pronoun.

1. The <u>Spartans</u> wrote a message on a belt wrapped around the length of a stick. _____

2. The <u>receiver</u> of the message unwound the belt. _____

3. The <u>message</u> could not be read unless it was again wound around the right size stick. _____

4. <u>Julius Caesar</u> invented a clever code. _____

5. The <u>code</u> was set up so that each letter of the message was substituted by a letter three places to the right. _____

6. <u>People</u> still use similar codes today. _____

7. <u>Students</u> can use this code. For example, CAT becomes FDW. _____

8. <u>Cardinal Richelieu</u> of France was a code-maker too. _____

9. The <u>code</u> depended upon a card with holes in it. _____

10. <u>Code-breakers</u> would have to hold it over an innocent-looking message. _____

11. The <u>holes</u> revealed the true message. _____

12. <u>Kids</u> can invent some sort of secret code too. _____

Replace each underlined noun with an object pronoun.

13. The cardinal invented a <u>code</u>. He invented _____.

14. The teacher asked the class to invent <u>codes</u>. The teacher asked the class to invent _____.

15. Allen challenged <u>Ronnie</u> to crack the <u>code</u>. Allen challenged _____ to crack _____.

16. Bonnie told <u>Dee</u> the secret message. Bonnie told _____ the secret message.

Try This! Review the code of Julius Caesar above. Write a secret message to a friend, family member, or classmate using the code. The challenge: Figure out the code and encode the message!

FS-30045 Grammar

Name _____

All About Possessive and Reflexive Pronouns

Possessive pronouns show who or what has something. **Possessive nouns** show ownership by using apostrophes: *Emily's class studies Columbus.* Replace *Emily's* with a possessive pronoun and the following sentence is created: *Her class studies Columbus.* The word *her* is a possessive pronoun. It refers to something that Emily has—*her class*. The possessive pronouns include **my, our, your, his, her, its, their** (all of which usually appear before a noun) and **mine, ours, yours, his, hers, theirs** (all of which can appear alone or after a verb).

Reflexive pronouns refer back to the pronoun and end in **self** (singular) or **selves** (plural): **myself, yourself, himself, herself, itself, ourselves, yourselves, themselves**. (Hint: *Hisself* and *theirselves* do not exist, so never use them!)

They really enjoyed themselves at the county fair.
You can thank yourself for the trouble you were in today.
He patted himself on the back. "Don't help me, I can do it myself."

Avoid mistakes such as *He and myself went together* instead of *He and I went together*.

Practice Makes Perfect

Write the correct possessive pronoun on the lines in the story below. (Hint: Each one will refer to the subject of the sentence before it.)

Sandra's calf won first prize at the County Fair. _____ calf was the best of show. Fred's calf won second prize. _____ calf wasn't as pretty as Sandra's. Cara and Fran's pumpkin bread tasted awful. _____ pumpkin bread tasted like cardboard. The calf's blue ribbon came off, and the pig ate it. _____ blue ribbon never made it home.

Circle the possessive pronouns in the paragraph below.

My entry in the pickle contest made two of the judges sick. They turned green and asked, "Are these your pickles?" I eagerly nodded my head and claimed my pickles. One of the judges just shook his head and declared, "Her pickles are weird. Their color is red, their taste is sweet. Look at this one. What is its problem?" I smiled. "That's my secret," I said proudly, "but I'll whisper it to you." The judge turned his head to my ear. "Kool-Aid!" he roared. "She put Kool-Aid in her pickles!" Now I can't use my secret ingredient anymore, because everybody knows what it is.

Try This!

Write a recipe for a food you know how to prepare. Substitute weird ingredients for some of the correct ones. Give it to a friend and ask if he or she knows what's wrong with the recipe.

FS-30045 Grammar

Pronoun Practice

Using pronouns correctly

Name _____

All About Using Pronouns Correctly

Pronouns are simple to use, but many people use them incorrectly. One common mistake is using **I** before a noun. (Example: *I and my mother went shopping.* This sentence is incorrect. The other person always comes first. *My mother and I went shopping.*)

Another decision to be made is whether to use **I** or **me** when talking about yourself and another person. *My mother and me went shopping* is incorrect. To decide whether to use **I** or **me**, drop the other person and see how it sounds. *I went shopping* is correct; *Me went shopping* is not. So *My mother and I went shopping* is correct. *Betsy and I sit next to each other,* not *Betsy and me sit next to each other.* *Are you waiting for Betsy and me?* not *Are you waiting for Betsy and I?* Remember, take away the other person and see if it sounds right.

Another rule with pronouns is the following: Don't add extra pronouns that you don't need. *Betsy, **she** said she was waiting for me.* Instead, try *Betsy said she was waiting for me.* The first *she* isn't needed.

Practice Makes Perfect

On the lines, write the correct pronoun in each sentence.

1. My friend Connie and _____ (I, me) always go skating together.

2. Connie says, "You and _____ (I, me) are best friends."

3. But sometimes she really tests her and _____ (me, my) friendship.

4. She always keeps _____ (I, me) and everybody else waiting.

5. Once, our friend Cheryl and _____ (I, me) waited for Connie for an hour.

6. _____ (She, Her) and _____ (I, me) were furious.

7. "Connie," I fumed, "Why did you keep Cheryl and _____ (I, me) waiting so long?"

8. "You and _____ (she, her) were late," Connie replied huffily.

9. It turned out that Cheryl and _____ (I, me) were waiting at the wrong mall!

10. Were Cheryl and _____ (me, my) faces red!

Correct each pronoun mistake by rewriting the sentence.

11. I and my dog had a big adventure.

_____

12. Him and me decided to take a walk in the woods.

_____

13. Well, I really didn't ask he, but I sort of dragged him along.

_____

Try This! Write a story about an adventure you shared with a friend.

© Frank Schaffer Publications, Inc.

16

FS-30045 Grammar

Name _____

All About Pronoun and Verb Agreement

Pronouns must agree with the verbs to which they refer. When verbs are used in the present tense, the pronoun **she**, **he**, or **it** makes the verb change a bit. *She (he, it) **sees** koalas when she visits Australia. See* has an *s* added to it. But in *We (you, they) see koalas when we visit Australia, see* has *no s* at the end.

The verb **to have** becomes **has** or **have** depending on the pronoun. *We **have** to see the koala*, not *We **has** to see the koala. I **have** to go to the zoo*, not *I **has** to go to the zoo*. The verb **to be** uses **is** and **are** in the present tense. *We **are** going to see koalas*, not *We **is** going to see koalas*.

Practice Makes Perfect

Correct each underlined verb below.

1. They <u>has</u> an important place in the island continent of Australia. _____

2. They <u>attracts</u> millions of visitors to Australia. _____

3. They <u>is</u> often called koala bears, but they <u>is</u> marsupials._____ _____

4. We <u>protects</u> this precious symbol of their country. _____

5. They <u>has</u> sharp, curved claws to protect themselves. _____

6. They <u>climbs</u> trees, often with their babies on their backs. _____

7. They only <u>eats</u> the leaves of eucalyptus trees. _____

8. We <u>is</u> going to have koalas at our zoo. _____

9. Their habitat <u>are</u> being destroyed for housing developments. _____

10. Killing koalas <u>have</u> been prohibited by law. _____

Circle the correct verbs and draw a line through the incorrect ones. Write the correct verbs above those that are incorrect.

     "We is going to have a good vacation this year, or I'll eat a bug," says Dad. We starts laughing because he say that every year. Every year, something go wrong. So we starts out for Lucky Fool Camp. The name are enough for my brother and me to know that this are going to be another weird vacation. On the way, Dad get us lost. My brother know how to get to the camp. He have a great sense of direction. We finally gets there and there's a big sign that says, "Sorry, we is closed due to mosquito infestation." That mean the place are swarming with mosquitoes. In case we doesn't believe, one bite me right away. What now? Dad look so disappointed until Mom say, "I knew this would happen so I've been saving money all year. Here is four plane tickets to Disney World!" Dad give each of us a big hug. We have our first great vacation!

Try This!   Write about the worst vacation you ever had. If you have never had a bad one, make up something!

FS-30045 Grammar

Tensing Up!

Name _____

All About Past, Present, and Future Verb Tenses

Verbs name an action in a sentence and also tell when the action happens. The **tense** of the verb tells when the action happens.

The **present tense** of a verb indicates that an action is happening now.

Example *Rabbits **are** popular pets.*
*Rabbits **hide** from predators.*

The **past tense** of a verb indicates that an action has already happened.

Example *Rabbits **were** not popular in the past.*
*The rabbits **hid** from the fox.*

Most verbs add **-ed** to form the past tense. Some verbs, such as *hide*, are irregular, and the past tense is different. If the verb ends in **e**, such as *bake*, just add **d** to form the past tense *baked*. The past tense of *have* is always *had*.

The **future tense** of a verb names an action that will take place in the future.

Example *Rabbits **will** remain popular in the future.*
*Rabbits **will** always hide from predators.*

The helping verb *will* is used to form the future tense. After **I** and **we**, *shall* may be used instead of *will*.

Practice Makes Perfect

Write *Past, Present,* or *Future* on the line following each sentence.

1. Rabbits are often called bunnies. _____

2. Rabbits were once classified as rodents. _____

3. Most rabbits live in a shallow hole called a form. _____

4. Most rabbits sleep during the day and eat from dusk to dawn. _____

5. Unfortunately, someone had the idea that rabbits might be tasty food. _____

6. Rabbits are near the bottom of the food chain. _____

7. Many people know that these lovely animals make good pets. _____

8. Each bunny has his or her own personality. _____

9. Watching a bunny's antics will make you laugh. _____

10. Perhaps someday rabbits will be enjoyed more as pets, not food. _____

Try This! Make a list of good and bad points about having a pet bunny.

Presently Perfect!

Present perfect tense

Name _____

All About the Present Perfect Tense

The **present perfect tense** is formed by using the present tense of the helping verb *to have* plus the past tense of the verb it helps. This combination is called the **past participle**. Together, the tense they form is called the **present perfect tense**.

has (present tense of helping verb) + **past participle of the action verb** = **the present perfect tense**

Example: *Our cousins* **have arrived** *at last.* The past tense of a verb shows a definite time something happened in the past. The present perfect tense shows an indefinite time when something happened and indicates that it may still be going on.

Example ▸ *The cruise ship arrived late.*
(definite: *Late* answers when it arrived.)
The cruise ship has arrived.
(indefinite: *It* has arrived at some time.)

(Hint: Be careful of mixing the two tenses.)

Example ▸ 1. *My dad told me to clean my room yesterday,* not
2. *My dad* **has** *told me to clean my room yesterday.*

Why is number 2 incorrect? In number 1, *yesterday* is a definite time.
In number 2, the helping verb *have* is used to show a definite time and breaks the rule.

Example ▸ *I finished my book today.* NOT *I have finished my book today.*
I have finished my book is fine as long as you don't mention *today*, which is a definite time.

Practice Makes Perfect

Read each sentence below. Decide whether or not it is correct. Draw a happy face if it is, and a sad face if it isn't. Next to each sentence, write the reason for your decision (definite, indefinite).

Example ▸ *People have arrived at their destinations by airplane for many years.*
Many years is not a definite time, so the helping verb *have* may be used.

1. The family watched the planes take off every Sunday. _____

2. Charles wanted to fly since the age of ten. _____

3. Millions of people seen the planes take off and later
   joined the passengers. _____

4. Dad said to Charles, "Your big day has arrived." _____

5. "I arranged a twenty-minute trip, just around the island." _____

6. The flight in the small plane had begun smoothly. _____

7. Suddenly, the flight changed from smooth to rough. _____

Try This! Write seven sentences in the present perfect tense about an adventure you or someone you know had.

© Frank Schaffer Publications, Inc.

19

FS-30045 Grammar

It's All in the Past!

Name _____

All About Past Participles of Irregular Verbs

Many verbs don't seem to follow the rules about forming past tense and past participles. For example, using the verb *to sit*, *sit* is the present tense, but *sitted* is NOT the past tense, and *have/has sitted* is not the past participle. The verb changes to *sat. I sat under that tree this afternoon* and *I have sat under that tree before.*

Some regular verbs are often mistakenly given incorrect forms. Example: *sneak, sneaked, has/have sneaked*—not *snuck. Think* is irregular, but the past tense is not *thunk,* it is *thought.* Some verbs, such as *hit* and *put,* remain the same in the present, past, and past participle.

Practice Makes Perfect

Look at the list of irregular verbs in the box.
The best way to learn them is to memorize them.

Verb	Past Tense	Past Participle
eat	ate	has/have eaten
throw	threw	has/have thrown
see	saw	has/have seen
know	knew	has/have known
go	went	has/have gone
come	came	has/have come
bring	brought	has/have brought
run	ran	has/have run
let	let	has/have let
break	broke	has/have broken
think	thought	has/have thought
say	said	has/have said
tell	told	has/have told

Write the correct form of the word in each sentence.

1. I have _____ people from many countries. (know)

2. He _____ from the bully who picked on him. (run)

3. We often have _____ that hard work will get you ahead. (say)

4. If you have _____ me a present, I hope it's something I don't have. (bring)

5. After he _____ the ball, he made a home run. (hit)

6. After he _____ of the idea, he _____ us about it. (think, tell)

7. She _____ him come in from the rain with wet boots. (let)

8. They have _____ that movie every day this week. (see)

9. If you have _____ for the money I owe you, it's right here. (come)

10. When we _____ to the store, there was a big sale. (go)

Try This!   Write five sentences using irregular verbs with their past participles.

They Flew Into History

Name _____

All About Action Verbs and Linking Verbs

Action verbs show action or something that is happening. Example: *Charles Lindbergh flew across the Atlantic Ocean to France.* What did the subject, *Charles Lindbergh*, do? He flew across the Atlantic. *Flew* is the action word. It's something the subject did.

Linking verbs don't show action. They connect, or link, the subject with one or more words in the predicate that tell something about the subject. Example: *Charles Lindbergh was the first man to fly solo nonstop across the Atlantic. Charles Lindbergh* is still the subject. What does the linking verb *was* tell about him? He was the first man to fly nonstop across the Atlantic Ocean.

Common linking verbs are forms of the verb be: **is**, **are**, **was**, **were**, **will**. Others are **appear**, **seem**, **become**, **use**.

Practice Makes Perfect

Read the paragraphs below about Charles Lindbergh and Amelia Earhart and their historic flights. Above each underlined verb, write *L* for linking verb or *A* for action verb.

Charles Lindbergh <u>was</u> one of the greatest heroes of the 1920s. Nowadays, his trip doesn't <u>seem</u> that exciting or important. But he <u>flew</u> just 24 years after the Wright brothers <u>made</u> the world's first flight. Flying <u>was</u> still very new when Lindbergh <u>decided</u> to risk his life crossing the Atlantic Ocean. The name of his famous plane <u>was</u> the *Spirit of St. Louis*. After a long trip over water, he <u>landed</u> at Le Bourget Field near Paris in 1927. The crowds <u>became</u> wild when they <u>saw</u> Lindbergh. Everyone <u>called</u> him "Lucky Lindy."

Amelia Earhart <u>crossed</u> the Atlantic Ocean too. She <u>was</u> the first woman to <u>do</u> so and <u>was</u> also the first woman to <u>do</u> it solo, or alone. The public <u>loved</u> Amelia, and she <u>became</u> famous throughout the world. In 1937, she <u>decided</u> to <u>fly</u> around the world. Her airplane <u>vanished</u> near Howland Island in the Pacific Ocean.

Neither she nor her plane <u>were</u> ever found. There <u>are</u> many theories about what happened to Amelia. Did the Japanese <u>capture</u> her? Did she <u>drown</u>? Did she <u>land</u> on a deserted island and <u>die</u> there? We'll probably never <u>know</u>. But Amelia Earhart <u>has</u> earned her place in history.

Try This! What do you think might have happened to Amelia Earhart? Some people think she never died but has been in hiding since her plane disappeared. Write what you think happened to her. Circle all the linking verbs in your story. Draw an action-packed illustration.

Try These Verbs!

Name _____

All About Transitive and Intransitive Verbs

How can you tell the difference between transitive and intransitive verbs? A **transitive verb** is
followed by a direct object, a word that often answers the question *what or whom.* (Example: *Our
ancestors cooked food. Cooked* is a transitive verb because it's followed by the word *food,* which
answers the question *what* and is the object of the verb.)

Our ancestors cooked. Cooked is an **intransitive verb** because it is not followed by an object.
It doesn't tell what our ancestors cooked. (Example: *People learned to make fire. Learned* is a
transitive verb because it is followed by an object, *to make fire.* It answers the question, *What did
they learn? People learned. Learned* is an intransitive verb since it's not followed by an object.)

Practice Makes Perfect

Read about our ancestors below. Next to each sentence, write *T* for transitive and *I* for intransitive
to indicate what the underlined verbs are.

1. People <u>cooked</u> food before they knew how to make fire. _____

2. They <u>cooked</u> meat over burning wood they found. _____

3. Our ancestors <u>hunted</u>. _____

4. They <u>hunted</u> some animals that are now extinct. _____

5. In Ancient Rome, people <u>cooked</u> food on raised hearths. _____

6. They <u>set</u> large kettles on tripods over the fire. _____

7. Some ancient people <u>broiled</u>. _____

8. They <u>held</u> food on a stick over a fire until it was done . _____

9. The stick was <u>turned</u>. _____

10. The food was soon <u>broiled</u> on all sides. _____

11. Hot coals <u>were</u> also used. _____

12. Pits were <u>dug</u>. _____

13. The pits were <u>lined</u> with hot rocks. _____

14. Our ancestors <u>built</u> fires on the rocks. _____

15. Some Indians of the American Southwest <u>heated</u> stones in the sun. _____

16. They <u>placed</u> food on the stones. _____

17. The sun <u>baked</u> the food. _____

18. The Romans <u>invented</u> a type of oven. _____

19. Many people <u>used</u> outdoor ovens for cooking and baking. _____

20. Indoor ovens <u>needed</u> chimneys for the smoke to go out. _____

Try This!

How do you think people will prepare food in the future? Will we still use stoves or
ovens? How about barbecues? Write at least one paragraph explaining your
theories.

FS-30045 Grammar

It's Agreed!

Name _____

All About Subject and Verb Agreement

A singular subject must have a singular verb as a partner. A plural subject must have a plural verb as a partner. (Example: *People are living longer in many countries. People* is a plural subject, so the plural verb *are* is used with it. *A person usually lives longer if he has good health habits. Person* is a singular subject, and *lives* is a singular verb.)

If two singular words appear together as compound subjects, the verb will be plural. *Hank and Sandy think they passed the test,* not *Hank and Sandy thinks they passed the test.* If a compound subject is joined with **either—or**, **neither—nor**, the verb must agree with the subject that is closer to the verb: *Neither my brother nor I think we look alike. Either my dog or my cats are making noise outside. Everyone who comes to my party is bringing a gift,* not *Everyone who comes to my party are bringing a gift.* Words such as **everyone**, **anyone**, **no one**, **somebody**, **someone**, **something** are called singular indefinite pronouns. They always require a singular verb.

Practice Makes Perfect

Write the correct verb form to match each subject in the story below.

Cormorants _____ (is, are) birds that help people. In some countries, this type of bird _____ (is, are) used to help catch fish! Great fishermen (or fisherbirds), cormorants _____ (fly, flies) around fishing grounds. Fishermen watching them know where the fish _____ (is, are). Some fishermen _____ (catch, catches) cormorants. They _____ (tie, ties) long cords to the birds, then _____ (take, takes) them out on their boats. When the birds _____ (dive, dives) under the water to catch fish, the fishermen _____ (keep, keeps) them from making off with the fish. Cormorants _____ (is, are) related to pelicans. Most cormorants _____ (perch, perches) in trees, on rocks, and on the edges of cliffs. They _____ (has, have) webbed feet.

Circle the correct verb in each sentence.

1. Those toys (is, are) loved by most children.

2. There (is, are) two kids who missed the bus.

3. Neither my cat nor my dogs (like, likes) to eat pet food.

4. There (is, are) no reasons for you to miss school today.

5. Facts (is, are) facts, and you can't deny them.

6. Many movie monsters (is, are) truly scary.

7. Either you or your sister (is, are) going to clean that room.

8. Five tomatoes (is, are) growing on the vine.

Try This! Write a story about an animal that is helpful to humans.

A Preposition Proposition

Name _____

All About Prepositional Phrases

Prepositional phrases begin with a preposition (i.e. **of**, **outside**, **inside**, **for**, **down**, **above**, **behind**, **with**, etc.) and end with a noun or pronoun. Example: *We saw a squirrel in the tree. Squirrel* is related to *tree* by the preposition *in.* The entire prepositional phrase is *in the tree. The squirrel ran around the park. Around the park* is the prepositional phrase. *Around* is the preposition.

Practice Makes Perfect

Circle the prepositional phrase(s) in each sentence. Underline the preposition.

1. Many animals live in trees.

2. Woodpeckers can be heard tapping on the bark of trees.

3. Termites make tasty treats for many animals.

4. Some insects that live inside hollow trees have destroyed the trees.

5. Trees with thick foliage provide camouflage for many creatures.

6. Fallen trees make cozy hiding places until their secret is discovered.

7. Many small animals live beneath the ground.

8. Flying squirrels silently glide between trees.

9. Birds fly over the highest trees.

10. Owls fly into the night, without making a sound.

11. Bats depend on their vision to find food at night.

12. The forest is a wondrous place with a huge animal population.

13. Ducks with their babies following waddle to and fro.

14. A family of raccoons looks for food.

15. The rabbit hides inside his burrow.

16. People with picnic baskets disturb the quiet.

17. The animals are shy and afraid of the people.

18. A bold chipmunk strolls around the picnic table.

19. He gets a handout with a smile.

20. It's fun to eat right beside the animals of the forest.

21. We must protect the forest from fire and other devastation.

22. We must make sure we can always take walks through the woods.

23. Then we will always be able to see the frog jump over the lily pad.

24. We can live beside the animals and appreciate them.

Try This! Make a list of forest animals. Include their houses, food, and other habits, such as hibernation, storing food, and ways of protecting themselves.

FS-30045 Grammar

Name _____

All About Who and Whom

Whom often sounds awkward, and many people don't feel comfortable using the word. **Who** is usually used as a subject: *Who will colonize Mars first? Whom* is usually used as the object of a preposition: *To whom will the glory belong?* One purpose of using the word **whom** is to prevent a sentence from ending in a preposition. Although a sentence that ends in a preposition is not incorrect, it is helpful to know how to speak and write placing prepositions in the beginning or middle of a sentence.

Practice Makes Perfect

Get ready for a trip to Mars as you decide whether to use *who* or *whom* in each sentence. Write the correct word.

1. To _____ would you write if you went to Mars?

2. _____ is brave enough to go to Mars?

3. From _____ has the government received applications for the trip?

4. _____ wants to go to a dead planet?

5. For _____ is space travel interesting?

6. With _____ would you like to go to the red planet?

7. _____ would be the boss if we established a colony?

8. There is a long list of people _____ would go in a minute.

9. Many people _____ want to go aren't qualified.

10. Do you know anyone _____ is qualified?

11. How would I know _____ is qualified?

12. Those _____ are qualified will receive first preference.

13. Do you know _____ really wants to go?

14. I know I do, that's _____!

15. But with _____ are you going?

16. I don't know, but those _____ take the first steps on Mars will be famous.

17. Well, I'll go with you then because my cousin, _____ is a writer, will write a book about our trip.

18. And anyone _____ is anyone will buy the book.

19. For _____ would we be going to Mars, anyway?

20. For the people of Earth, that's for _____!

Try This!

Write a resume telling why you should be on the first manned flight to Mars. Don't forget to include all your qualifications.

Dandy Descriptions

Name _____

All About Adjectives, Adjective Subjects, and Adjective Predicates

Adjectives describe nouns or pronouns. *I like ice cream.* This sentence isn't nearly as interesting as *I like cold, creamy, fudgy ice cream.* All the words that describe ice cream are adjectives.

The playful puppy dove into the pile of leaves. The subject, *puppy,* is described by the adjective *playful. The puppy dove into the crinkly fall leaves.* In this sentence, the predicate contains the adjective. Of course, both subject and predicate can often benefit from adjectives.

Practice Makes Perfect

Read the story about cowboys below. Underline all the subject adjectives, and circle all the predicate adjectives you find.

Rugged cowboys are part of the legend of the American West. According to these legends, cowboys' lives were full of dangerous trails, sad songs, and faithful horses. Some modern cowboys prefer to be called cowhands, because they are hired workers, or hands, who look after cows. Western cowboys became well-known after the Civil War. These strong men worked on big and small ranches in Texas, Montana, Wyoming, and other western states. Their days were hard, long, and dirty. It was hard for a cowboy to make a permanent home, as he was often away on cattle drives for months at a time.

A loyal, strong horse meant everything to a cowboy. Smart cowboys took good care of their wonderful horses, who often actually saved their masters' lives. The conquering Spanish brought the useful horse back to America. The horse lived in America during prehistoric times, but became extinct. Today, wild horses also roam the Wild West. Sometimes they are rounded up, and people buy them for many reasons. Some become lucky pets for horse-loving children.

Yesterday's cowboy slept on the hard ground at night. He ate stale bread, greasy bacon, and biscuits, and drank coffee from tin cups. Cowboys hardly knew what fresh fruit or vegetables looked like. Modern cowboys may use metal machinery that the original cowboys never dreamed about. But they still need a good horse, they must be able to work long hours, and they must have a sense of old-fashioned adventure.

Write an interesting adjective to describe each noun.

1. Most cowboys led a _____ life.

2. _____ horses were important to cowboys.

3. Cowboys often ate _____ food.

4. The _____ trail took a long time to complete.

5. _____ cowboys often use trucks in their work.

Try This! Would you like the life of a cowboy? Why or why not? Why do you think anyone would want to be a cowboy in this day and age? Write your answers on the back of this page.

FS-30045 Grammar

Pronoun Perfection

Name _____

All About Pronouns and Object Pronouns

A **pronoun** can replace a noun or nouns used as the object of a verb. **Subject pronouns** replace subjects. Example: *John collected eggs from the henhouse. He collected eggs from the henhouse. He* replaces *John* as the subject.

The object of a verb receives the action of the verb. It answers the question *whom* or *what* after an action verb. *Carole found money. Carole found it. It* replaces the noun *money.* **Object pronouns** are used as the objects of verbs. **Me**, **us**, **you**, **him**, **her**, **it**, and **them** are object pronouns.

Practice Makes Perfect

Replace each underlined noun with an object pronoun. Circle the verb that the object pronoun follows.

1. Thomas Edison invented <u>lightbulbs</u>. _____

2. Sleep meant nothing to <u>Edison</u>. _____

3. He often went without <u>dinner</u>. _____

4. He worried <u>Mrs. Edison</u>. _____

5. The invention made money for <u>the family</u>. _____

6. Edison was proud of <u>many patents</u>. _____

7. Mrs. Edison was probably proud of <u>her husband</u>. _____

Circle each subject pronoun.

8. He was known as "The Wizard of Menlo Park."

9. He and Mrs. Edison lived in a town in New Jersey.

10. They had an unusual life.

11. He had thought of inventing since he was a little boy.

12. He was especially proud of inventing the phonograph.

13. He came close to inventing the radio.

14. We should be very grateful to Thomas Alva Edison.

15. He improved the inventions of others, too.

16. I greatly admire this American genius.

17. Can you think of anyone who was a greater inventor?

Use each object pronoun in a sentence. Remember, they are as follows: **me**, **you**, **him**, **her**, **it**, **us**, and **them**. Write the sentences on the back of this page.

Try This! What is left to invent? Make a list of 10 things you wish someone would invent. Tell why you think those inventions are needed by humankind.

That's Correct!

Name _____

All About Using Words Correctly

Many words in English are often confused with each other because they sound alike or almost alike. Choosing the correct word is important in school and in your future.
Study the words and their differences below.

their—*Their dog ran down the street after the mailman.*
they're (contraction for *they are*)—*They're going to be sorry if their dog bites him.*
there—*There must be a way to stop that dog from chasing poor Mr. Flint.*

your—*Your dog likes to bring in the mail.*
you're (contraction of *you are*)—*You're responsible for your dog's behavior.*

there's (contraction of *there is*)—*There's an obedience class for your dog.*
theirs (shows ownership)—*"Yes, Mr. Flint, that dog is theirs."*

its (pronoun)—*The dog gave its paw to Mr. Flint.*
it's (contraction of *it is*)—*It's going to be all right now.*

Practice Makes Perfect

Circle the correct words below and write them in the blanks provided.

1. _____ too bad that dogs can't talk. (It's, Its)

2. That dog would bite _____ master if it had the chance. (its, it's)

3. You just don't know _____ dog, Wally. (there, their)

4. I saw him over _____, waiting for trouble. (there, their)

5. Well, _____ crazy about _____ dog. (there, they're, their)

6. When I see him _____ , I cross the street. (their, there)

7. _____ saying that because you don't know him. (You're, Your)

8. If he was _____ dog, you'd feel differently. (you're, your)

9. _____ time to go because he's coming over here. (It's, Its)

10. He's licking _____ face! (your, you're)

11. _____ face looks like _____ smiling! (It's, Its)

12. _____ now, you owe him an apology. (There, Their)

13. _____ true; he's a nice dog! (It's, Its)

Try This!   Write a letter to someone you admire. Use each of the above words at least once.

FS-30045 Grammar

Name _____

Types of Sentences

For each sentence below, write what type it is next to it. Remember, your choices are *declarative*, *interrogative, exclamatory,* and *imperative.*

1. Open the closet and take down those boxes.

2. Do you see the boxes on the top shelf?

3. They're falling on your head!

4. I think it's time to clean the closet.

Subjects and Predicates

Underline the simple subject in each sentence. Circle the complete predicate.

5. Summer fruits are the best.

6. You have a great choice during the summer.

7. Plums, grapes, and peaches are just a few of the summer fruits available.

8. Farmers' markets have the freshest fruits.

9. They say the fruit has just been picked that day.

10. I always leave with a bagful.

11. My day always begins with fresh fruit.

Compound Predicates

Connect the two sentences in each exercise with *either, and*, or, *but.*

12. Mesopotamia was an ancient land. It was in the Middle East.

13. Mesopotamia has a meaning. It means *between rivers.*

14. The two rivers are the Tigris and the Euphrates. The land there was fertile.

15. Mesopotamia was the site of great civilizations. They didn't last.

16. Writing was invented in Mesopotamia. This writing system used word-pictures.

Adjectives

Write an appropriate adjective to complete each sentence.

17. The _____ moon shone brightly last night.

18. It's fun to swim in the _____ ocean.

19. Sky-diving is a _____ sport.

20. The _____, _____ cow stood grazing in the field all day.

21. I like to stay inside on a _____, _____ day.

⟨29⟩

More Rave Reviews

Name _____

Common, Proper, and Collective Nouns

Write a common, proper, or collective noun in each sentence.

1. The name of the President of the United States is _____.

2. The man who is buried in Grant's Tomb is _____.

3. The _____ of geese honked as it crossed the road.

4. Three domesticated animals are _____, _____, and _____.

5. The _____ of lions lay in the hot sun.

6. One of the seven continents is _____.

Possessive Nouns

Rewrite the sentences below to make each underlined noun possessive. Change any words if necessary so that the sentences make sense.

7. The songs of <u>whales</u> are beautiful and eerie.

   _____

8. The habits of <u>whales</u> are interesting.

   _____

9. Captains of whaling <u>ships</u> killed many whales each year.

   _____

10. The ships of some <u>captains</u> have been struck by blue whales.

    _____

11. Some <u>captains</u> have good luck, and they don't drown.

    _____

Run-On Sentences

Rewrite the story below so that there are no run-on sentences.

    Do you have a best friend I do and her name is Caitlin and we have been friends for a long time and she helps me when I need help and I help her too and sometimes I think we share the same thoughts and we're in the same class and we even get the same grades and we don't even try to do that and we will be best friends forever I hope.

_____

_____

_____

_____

_____

Sentence Fragments

Change the sentence fragments below to make complete sentences.

12. Computers are. Important machines. _____

13. They are used in businesses. And schools. _____

14. Computers have been around. For a long time. _____

30

Answers

Page 2
1. declarative 2. interrogative
3. interjection 4. imperative
5. interrogative 6. declarative
7. interrogative 8. interrogative
9. imperative 10. exclamatory
11. imperative 12. declarative

Page 3
underline=subject; bold=predicate
<u>cats</u>, **are**, <u>people</u>, **buy**, <u>they</u>, **buy**, <u>cats</u>, **are not**, <u>Egyptians</u>, **worshiped**, <u>felines</u>, **were**, <u>Egyptians</u>, **built**, <u>many</u>, **buried**, <u>cats</u>, **were**, <u>families</u>, **kept**, <u>cats</u>, **were**, <u>cats</u>, **have**, <u>they</u>, **are**, <u>they</u>, **are**, <u>cats</u>, **should not be**, <u>they</u>, **should be**
1. <u>cows</u> **are sacred animals.**
2. <u>cows</u> **are not to be bothered as they roam the streets.**
3. <u>Cows</u> **are not eaten as food in India.**
4. <u>The expression "sacred cow"</u> **has come to mean someone or something that is not to be questioned, that must be accepted.**
5. <u>There are many varieties of cows</u> **throughout the world.**

Page 4
underline=subject; bold=predicate
1. **Are** <u>starlings</u> **native to North America?**
2. **Did** <u>you</u> **hear the birds chirping in the morning?**
3. **Do** <u>you</u> **leave birdseed out for them?**
4. **Did** <u>you</u> **know that the passenger pigeon is extinct?**
5. **Is** <u>it</u> **true that the ostrich cannot fly?**
6. **Are** <u>falcons</u> **still found in the wild?**
7. **Is** <u>it</u> **true that eagles and hawks have the keenest sight of all birds?**
8. **Are** <u>most bald eagles</u> **found in Alaska?**
9. **Did** <u>the dodo</u> **become extinct because it was stupid?**
10. **Did** <u>birds</u> **exist with dinosaurs?**
11. you 12. you 13. you
14. you 15. you

Page 5
1. The Spanish and a Moorish slave named Estevanico looked for the Seven Cities of Cibola.
2. Francisco Coronado and Estevanico led expeditions.
3. The Moor and the Spaniard hoped to find riches.
4. Estevanico and Coronado explored Arizona and New Mexico.
5. Coronado found no riches and returned to Mexico.
6. The Zuñi Indians live in the Southwest United States and are found in present-day Gallup, New Mexico.
7. The Spanish believed in a fairy tale and followed a legend about the Seven Cities of Cibola.

Page 6
Sentences will vary.

Page 7
Sentences will vary.

Page 8
thousand, thousands; year, years; dress, dresses; pant, pants; shirt, shirts; form, forms; item, items; skin, skins; skin, skins; animal, animals; fox, foxes; buffalo, buffalo(s)(es); bear, bears; day, days; part, parts; costume, costumes; kilt, kilts; skirt, skirts; dress, dresses; material, materials; garment, garments; factory, factories; lady, ladies

Page 9
1. calves 2. Mice 3. moose
4. teeth 5. women 6. deer
7. chiefs 8. children 9. sheep
10. halves 11. feet 12. loaves
13. Babies 14. Mice 15. thieves
16. waltzes 17. churches 18. dishes

Page 10
1. Clouds are important to the changes in weather. p, s
2. Clouds bring necessary rainfall and snow to provide water. p, s
3. Clouds come in many different forms. p, s
4. White fluffy clouds often take the form of familiar shapes. p, s
5. Menacing-looking gray or black clouds look threatening. s, p; s
6. Most clouds change their shape all the time. p, s
7. Stratus and stratocumulus clouds are seen close to Earth. p, s
8. Some middle clouds that form smooth gray sheets across the sky are called altostratus clouds. p, s
9. Other middle clouds like altocumulus clouds appear in many shapes. p, s
10. High clouds such as cirrus, cirrostratus, and cirrocumulus are formed of ice crystals. p, s
11. f 12. s
13. s 14. f

Page 11
Sentences will vary.

Page 12
1. Esther Forbes's
2. America's
3. colonists'
4. George Washington's
5. Indians'
6. settlers'
7. Betsy's
8. England's
9. Germans'
10. children's

Page 13
bold=common nouns, underline=proper nouns
1. **house**, <u>President of the United States</u>, White House
2. **statue, torch, color**, Statue of Liberty
3. <u>Washington, D. C.,</u> **stone**, Vietnam Veterans Memorial
4. **television shows, guests**, Green Room
5. **river**, <u>Austria</u>, **music**, Danube
6. **river, boundary**, <u>Oklahoma, Texas,</u> Red River
7. **forest, tourist destination**, <u>Germany</u>, Black Forest
8. **cartoon character, TV**, Pink Panther
9. **country, ice, snow, name**, Greenland
10. **person, world**, <u>American flag</u>, Robert Gray
11. pack 12. tribe
13. flock 14. school
15. crowd 16. stack

Page 14
1. they 2. he/she 3. it
4. he 5. it 6. they
7. they 8. he 9. it
10. they 11. they 12. they
13. it 14. them 15. him, it
16. her

Page 15
Her, His, Their, Its;
My, your, my, my, his, Her, Their, their, its, my, his, my, her, my

Answers

Page 16
1. I   2. I   3. my
4. me   5. I   6. She, I
7. me   8. she   9. I   10. my
11. My dog and I had a big adventure.
12. He and I decided to take a walk in the woods.
13. Well, I really didn't ask him, but I sort of dragged him along.

Page 17
1. have   2. attract
3. are, are   4. protect
5. have   6. climb
7. eat   8. are
9. is   10. has
are, start, says, goes, start, is, is, gets, knows, has, get, are, means, is, don't, bites, looks, says, are, gives

Page 18
1. present   2. past
3. present   4. present
5. past   6. present
7. present   8. present
9. future   10. future

Page 19
1. happy, definite   2. happy, definite
3. sad, indefinite   4. happy, indefinite
5. happy, definite   6. happy, indefinite
7. happy, definite

Page 20
1. known   2. ran
3. said   4. brought
5. hit   6. thought, told
7. let   8. seen
9. come   10. went

Page 21
was—L, seem—L, flew—A, made—A, was—L, decided—A, was—L, landed—A, became—L, saw—A, called—A, crossed—A, was—L, do—A, was—L, do—A, loved—A, became—L, decided—A, fly—A, vanished—A, were—L, are—L, capture—A, drown—A, land—A, die—A, know—A, has—L

Page 22
1. T   2. T   3. I   4. T
5. T   6. T   7. I   8. T
9. I   10. T   11. I   12. I
13. T   14. T   15. T   16. T
17. T   18. T   19. T   20. T

Page 23
are, is, fly, are, catch, tie, take, dive, keep, are, perch, have
1. are   2. are   3. like
4. are   5. are   6. are
7. is   8. are

Page 24
1. <u>in</u> trees
2. <u>on</u> the bark, <u>of</u> trees
3. <u>for</u> many animals
4. <u>inside</u> hollow trees
5. <u>with</u> thick foliage, <u>for</u> many creatures
6. <u>until</u> their secret
7. <u>beneath</u> the ground
8. <u>between</u> trees
9. <u>over</u> the highest trees
10. <u>into</u> the night, <u>without</u> making a sound
11. <u>on</u> their vision
12. <u>with</u> a huge animal population
13. <u>with</u> their babies
14. <u>of</u> raccoons, <u>for</u> food
15. <u>inside</u> his burrow
16. <u>with</u> picnic baskets
17. <u>of</u> the people
18. <u>around</u> the picnic table
19. <u>with</u> a smile
20. <u>beside</u> the animals, <u>of</u> the forest
21. <u>from</u> fire and other devastation
22. <u>through</u> the woods
23. <u>over</u> the lily pad
24. <u>beside</u> the animals

Page 25
1. whom   2. Who   3. whom
4. Who   5. whom   6. whom
7. Who   8. who   9. who
10. who   11. who   12. who
13. who   14. who   15. whom
16. who   17. who   18. who
19. whom   20. whom

Page 26
underlined=subject adjectives,
bold=predicate adjectives
<u>Rugged</u>, **American, dangerous, sad, faithful,** <u>modern</u>, **hired,** <u>Western</u>, <u>strong</u>, **big, small, western, hard, long, dirty, permanent, cattle,** <u>loyal</u>, <u>strong</u>, <u>Smart</u>, **good, wonderful,** <u>conquering</u>, **useful, prehistoric,** <u>wild</u>, **many, lucky, horse-loving,** <u>Yesterday's</u>, **hard, stale, greasy, tin, fresh,** <u>Modern</u>, **metal, original, good, long, old-fashioned**
1.-5. Answers will vary.

Page 27
1. them, invented   2. him, meant
3. it, went   4. her, worried
5. them, made   6. them, was proud
7. him, was proud   8. He
9. He   10. They   11. He, he
12. He   13. He   14. We
15. He   16. I   17. you

Page 28
1. It's   2. its
3. their   4. there
5. they're, their   6. there
7. You're   8. your
9. It's   10. your
11. Its, it's   12. There   13. It's

Page 29
1. imperative   2. interrogative
3. exclamatory   4. declarative
5. <u>fruits</u> **are the best**
6. <u>You</u> **have a great choice during the summer.**
7. <u>Plums, grapes, and peaches</u> **are just a few of the summer fruits available.**
8. <u>Farmers' markets</u> **have the freshest fruits.**
9. <u>They</u> **say the fruit has just been picked that day.**
10. <u>I</u> **always leave with a bagful.**
11. <u>My day</u> **always begins with fresh fruit.**
12. Mesopotamia was an ancient land, and it was in the Middle East.
13. Mesopotamia has a meaning, and it means *between rivers*.
14. The two rivers are the Tigris and the Euphrates, and the land there was fertile.
15. Mesopotamia was the site of great civilizations, but they didn't last.
16. Writing was invented in Mesopotamia, and this writing system used word-pictures.
17.-21. Answers will vary.

Page 30
1. *Name of current President*
2. President Grant
3. gaggle
4. Answers will vary.
5. pride
6. Answers will vary.
7.-11. Accept reasonable answers. Some suggestions follow.
7. Whales' songs are beautiful and eerie.
8. Whales' habits are interesting.
9. Whaling ships' captains killed many whales each year.
10. Some captains' ships have been struck by blue whales.
11. Some captains' luck is good, and they don't drown.
Sentences will vary.
12. Computers are important machines.
13. They are used in businesses and schools.
14. Computers have been around for a long time.

FS-30045 Grammar